Really Easy Guitar!

Bryan Adams

GW00684952

Wise Publications
London/New York/Paris/Sydney/
Copenhagen/Madrid/Tokyo

Contents

1 **Introduction** 3

2 **Kids Wanna Rock** 8

3 **Run To You** 12

4 **Somebody** 16

5 **Summer Of '69** 20

6 **(Everything I Do) I Do It For You** 24

7 **Can't Stop This Thing We Started** 28

8 **Have You Ever Really Loved A Woman?** 32

9 **(I Wanna Be) Your Underwear** 36

10 **The Only Thing That Looks Good On Me Is You** 40

11 **18 Till I Die** 44

12 **When You're Gone** 48

13 **Cloud Number 9** 52

Further Reading 56

Exclusive distributors:
Music Sales Limited
8/9 Frith Street, London W1D 3JB, England.
Music Sales Pty Limited
120 Rothschild Avenue, Rosebery, NSW 2018,
Australia.

Order No. AM971806
ISBN: 0-7119-9060-3
This book ©2001 by Wise Publications

Thanks to Andrea Mills and Bryan Adams for
their help and co-operation

Written and arranged by Joe Bennett
Music Processed by The Pitts and Paul Ewers
Edited by Sorcha Armstrong
Book design by Chloë Alexander
Cover and book photographs courtesy of LFI/
Redferns and Bryan Adams' personal collection
Pages 3-6 photographs by George Taylor

Printed in the United Kingdom by
Printwise (Haverhill) Limited, Haverhill, Suffolk.

CD mastered by Jonas Persson
All guitars by Arthur Dick
Bass by Paul Townsend
Drums by Ian Thomas
Additional programming by John Moores

Your Guarantee of Quality
As publishers, we strive to produce every book to
the highest commercial standards.
 The music has been freshly engraved and the
book has been carefully designed to minimise
awkward page turns and to make playing from it a
real pleasure. Particular care has been given to
specifying acid-free, neutral-sized paper made
from pulps which have not been elemental
chlorine bleached. This pulp is from farmed
sustainable forests and was produced with special
regard for the environment.
 Throughout, the printing and binding have
been planned to ensure a sturdy, attractive
publication which should give years of enjoyment.
If your copy fails to meet our high standards,
please inform us and we will gladly replace it.

Music Sales' complete catalogue describes
thousands of titles and is available in full colour
sections by subject, direct from Music Sales
Limited. Please state your areas of interest and
send a cheque/postal order for £1.50 for postage
to: Music Sales Limited, Newmarket Road,
Bury St. Edmunds, Suffolk IP33 3YB.

Got any comments?
e-mail reallyeasyguitar@musicsales.co.uk

Introduction

Welcome to Really Easy Guitar, a fantastic new way to learn the songs you love.

This book will teach you how to play 12 classic songs – and you don't even have to be able to read music!

Inside you will find lyrics and chords for each song, complete with the chord shapes you need to start playing immediately. There's a special introduction to each song, with helpful hints and playing tips. Fretboxes and guitar TAB teach you the famous riffs and patterns that everyone will recognise.

The accompanying 13-track CD features professionally recorded soundalike versions of each song – vocals have been left off so that you can sing along.

Just follow the simple four step guide to using this book and you will be ready to play along with your favourite musician!

1 Tune Your Guitar

Before you can start to play along with the backing tracks, you'll need to make sure that your guitar is in tune with the CD. Track 1 on the CD gives you notes to tune to for each string, starting with the top E string, and then working downwards.

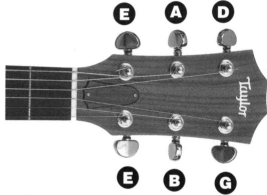

Alternatively, tune the bottom string first and then tune all the other strings to it.

Follow the tuning diagram below and tune from the bottom string upwards.

6th to 5th string	5th to 4th string	4th to 3rd string	3rd to 2nd string	2nd to 1st string

2 Understanding fretbox diagrams

Throughout this book, fretbox diagrams are used to show chord shapes and scale patterns. Think of the box as a view of the fretboard from head on – the thickest (lowest) string is on the left and the thinnest (highest) string is on the right.

The horizontal lines correspond to the frets on your guitar; the circles indicate where you should place your fingers.

An x above the box indicates that that string should not be played; an o indicates that the string should be played open.

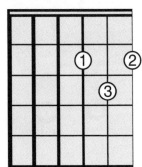

Hence, when playing this chord of D, make sure that you don't hit the bottom two strings.

All the chords you need for each song are given at the top of the song, in the order that they appear in that song.

Am   Am/G   D9/F♯   F

Shapes that are played higher up the neck are described in the same way – the lowest fret used is indicated to the left of the box. A curved line above the box shows that a first finger barre should be used.

This barre chord of G is played at the third fret, with the first finger stretching across all six strings.

3 Understanding scale patterns

We can also use chord box diagrams to show you certain useful scale patterns on the fretboard. When a box is used to describe a scale pattern, suggested fingerings are also included.

Black circles show you the root note of the scale. If the root note of the scale is an open string, this is indicated by a double circle. Grey circles represent notes of the scale below the lowest root note.

So in this example, the root note of the scale is the open D string, with another D appearing at the third fret on the B string.

4 Understanding TAB

TAB is another easy way to learn the famous riffs and hooks in each song. The six horizontal lines represent the six strings of the guitar – the lowest line represents the lowest string (low E), while the highest line represents the highest string (high E). The number on each line tells you which fret should be played.

Although we've also included traditional music notation, you don't actually need to be able to read music to use TAB – just listen to the recording and follow the fret positions on the TAB and you'll soon be playing along. There are certain special symbols which are used:

Hammer-on

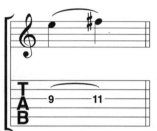

Look out for a slur connecting two numbers – when the second number is higher than the first this is called a "hammer-on". Place one finger at the lower of the two frets indicated and pick that string, then, without picking the string again, place your next finger at the higher fret. You should hear a smooth change in sound between the two notes.

Pull-off

A Pull-off is the opposite of a hammer-on, and is denoted by a slur joining two TAB numbers, where the second number is lower than the first one.

Place your fingers at the two fret positions indicated, and pick the first (higher) note, then simply lift the top finger, without picking the string again, allowing the bottom note to ring out.

Slide

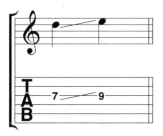

A slide between two notes is denoted by a short line in the TAB. Simply play the first note, and then move your finger to the new fret position by sliding it along the fretboard, restriking the string as you arrive at the new position.

Legato slide

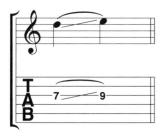

A legato slide is exactly the same as a normal slide, except that the second note is not picked again.

Bend

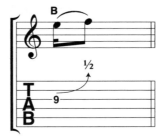

String bends are indicated as shown above – the amount that you need to bend the string is indicated near the arrow and could be ¼ tone (a decorative bend), ½ tone (the equivalent of one fret) or 1 tone (the equivalent of two frets).

Palm Muting

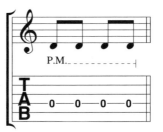

To get this percussive effect, place the side of your picking hand against the strings near the bridge as you pick.

2 **Kids Wanna Rock**

THIS UP-TEMPO crowd-pleaser was written by Bryan with long-time songwriting partner Jim Vallance, and appeared on his breakthrough 1985 album *Reckless*. Although it was never a single, it's such a favourite with the fans at gigs that it's amongst his best-known tracks.

▼ **C minor pentatonic scale**

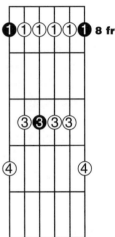

How to play it
The song opens with a classic 'riff-till-ready' intro (see TAB), before going into the verse, which is a straight-ahead rock 12-bar blues in E. Although the chords shown are 'power chords' (e.g. E5, A5 etc), Bryan is usually just playing regular open chord shapes (E, A etc), but using downstrokes with the plectrum and hitting only two or three bass strings of the chords. This helps to give more of an aggressive, driving rock feel to the electric rhythm guitar part.

The main riff
The bluesy riff makes substantial use of open strings, which can be difficult to play accurately at this speed without catching unwanted notes. As with all difficult guitar parts, practise slowly and gradually build up speed. The first note of the riff and the chords in the second bar both make use of 'off beat' timing. Listen to the CD several times to get the exact feel of this – wait for 8 clicks, then a very short rest, then play the 'double-stop' open strings that form the start of the riff.

Guitar solo
Despite the simple chord structure of the song, it's not possible to improvise a solo over these chords just using one simple scale shape. Lead guitarist Keith Scott starts the solo with notes taken from the C minor pentatonic scale (see fretbox) then changes soloing position along with the chords during almost every bar for the rest of the solo. If you're less confident at moving around the neck at speed, you could try playing notes from the E minor pentatonic scale (the same shape as C minor pentatonic but at the 12th fret) for the whole solo.

Guitar sound
Bryan is most commonly associated with the Fender Stratocaster, but for a straightforward rock track like this, any solid-body electric guitar should fit the bill. Select a bridge pickup setting with the guitar's tone up full, and set the distortion/gain control on your amp or pedal to about half. The song features a wah-wah pedal on many of the solos. If you decide to use one yourself, don't fall into the usual trap of tapping your foot on it in time with the music. The wah should be a slow movement from bass to treble while you're soloing. Add a delay effect with the mix set to around 40%, feedback to 20% and the delay time to 300-400ms.

▼ Main riff

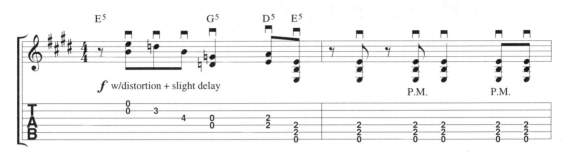

Kids Wanna Rock

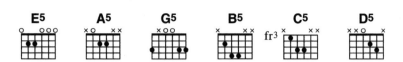

Words & Music by Bryan Adams & Jim Vallance

E5   A5   G5   B5   fr3 C5   D5

Intro   ‖: E5 | E5   :‖   *Play 6 times*

Verse 1

E5   A5
Turned on the radio,

E5   G5
Sounded like a disco,

A5
Must've turned the dial for a couple of miles

    E5
But I couldn't find no rock'n' roll.

Chorus 1

      B5
This computerised crap ain't gettin' me off,

E5
Everywhere I go the kids wanna rock.

Verse 2

E5
London to L.A.,

Talkin' 'bout the new wave.

    A5
For a couple of bucks you get a weird haircut

    E5   G5
And waste your life away.

Chorus 2

   B5
Around the world or around the block,

E5
Everywhere I go the kids wanna rock.

Bridge

G5
Get me my D.J.,

A5
I got somethin' he's gotta play.

C5
Wanna hear it, I can't wait,

D5
So turn it up, turn it up…

Solo

C5	C5	A5	A5	
E5	E5	E5	E5	
C5	C5	A5	A5	
B5	B5	B5	B5	‖
‖: E5	E5	E5	E5	:‖ *Play 4 times*

Verse 3

N.C.
Kick down the barricades,

E5
Listen to what the kids say.

A5
From time to time people change their minds

E5
But the music is here to stay.

Chorus 3

B5
I've seen it all, from the bottom to the top,

E5
Everywhere I go kids wanna rock.

Coda

B5
Around the world or around the block,

E5   **B5**
Everywhere I go the kids wanna rock,

E5   **N.C.**
Everywhere I go the kids wanna rock.

3 Run To You

ALTHOUGH BRYAN'S FIRST UK single reached only number 11 in 1985, that chiming chorused riff has since become one of the most instantly recognisable in the whole guitar shop repertoire. Like many great rock guitar riffs, it's actually easier to play than it sounds, which for most players has got to be a Good Thing.

How to play it

Bryan has been asked many times about the tuning for 'Run To You'. Here's his definitive answer: "The mystery of this track is it was recorded with a capo on the second fret, hence the F♯ tuning." So there you go – if you're going to play along to the CD you'll need a capo at the second fret. Even if you're an experienced player who can cope with barre chords, it's still worth using a capo – the chords and main riff just don't sound right using fretted notes only. Note that the chord sheet shows the chords in the key of E minor (i.e. the open chord shapes you should play if you're using a capo). The actual sound of the song is in the key of F♯ minor due to the capo.

The main riff

The riff is played using a plectrum, and each note is allowed to 'let ring' into the next. To play the first bar, hold down the 2nd fret of the fifth string with your second finger, and then pick across the strings with the plectrum in the order shown in the TAB, letting the strings ring out as much as possible. In bar 2, reach your third finger over to fret the sixth string at the 3rd fret while you pick the first three notes of the bar. Then move your fretting fingers up two frets and pick the remaining five notes of the bar. Once you can play this two bar loop over and over, you can get through the whole of the intro and first verse.

The rhythm guitar part

When you're playing the main chorus chords of Em, G, D and A, don't be tempted to strum up and downstrokes all the time. Listen to the CD and you'll hear that Bryan and Keith play a particular rhythmic pattern that accents certain chords. The timing of this is easier to get right when you know that all of the accented chords are played with an upstroke of the strumming hand.

Guitar sound

Only in the 1980s could a rock guitarist get away with using a distortion and chorus pedal at the same time, but if you want authenticity, these are the two effects you need. Switch the distortion off for the picked intro, then back on again just before you hit the C chord "when it gets too much". Use the middle pickup switch setting, and a medium drive or gain setting – if the level of distortion is too high the chords may lose definition. All of the guitars on our CD recording feature reverb, and you may want to add subtle 'slap-back' delay of around 200-300ms.

▼ Main riff

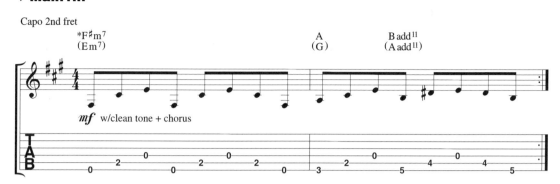

"The mystery of this track is it was recorded with a capo on the second fret, hence the F♯ tuning."

3 Run To You

Words & Music by Bryan Adams & Jim Vallance

Chord diagrams: Em7 | G | Aadd11 (fr5) | C5 (fr3) | D5 (fr5) | Em

G5 | D | A5 | E | C | Bm7

Capo second fret

Intro
(riff)

‖: Em7 | G Aadd11 | Em7 | G Aadd11 :‖

Verse 1

Em7(riff)   G   Aadd11 Em7   G Aadd11
She says her love for me could never die,

Em7   G   Aadd11
But that'd change if she ever found out

       Em7   G Aadd11
About you and I.

Em7   G   Aadd11
Oh, but her love is cold,

Em7   G   Aadd11
It wouldn't hurt her if she didn't know, 'cause

C5
When it gets too much

D5   Bm7
I need to feel your touch.

Chorus 1

            Em   G5 D A5
I'm gonna run to you,

            Em   G5 D A5
I'm gonna run to you,

                Em   G5   D   A5
'Cause when the feeling's right, I'm gonna run all night,

            Em   G5 D
I'm gonna run to you.

| Em7 | G Aadd11 | Em7 | G Aadd11 |

Verse 2

Em7(riff)　　　G　　　　　Aadd11　　　　Em7　　　　　G　Aadd11
　She's got a heart of gold, she'd never let me down,

Em7　　　　　　　　　　　　　　G　　　　　Aadd11
　But you're the one that always turns me on,

　　　　　　　Em7　　　　　G　Aadd11
You keep me comin' round.

Em7　　　　G　　　　　Aadd11
　I know her love is true

　　　　Em7　　　　　　　　G　　　　　Aadd11
But it's so damn easy makin' love to you,

C5
　I got my mind made up,

D5　　　　　Bm7
　I need to feel your touch.

Chorus 2

　　　　　　　　Em　　　　　G5　D
　I'm gonna run to you,

　A5　　　　　Em　　　　　G5　D　A5
‖: 　I'm gonna run to you,

　　　　　　　　Em　　　G5　　　　　D　　　　A5
'Cause when the feeling's right, I'm gonna run all night,

　　　　　　　Em　　　　　G5　D
I'm gonna run to you. 　　　　　　:‖

Solo

| E 　　| E 　　| D 　　| D 　　|

| C 　　| C 　　| D 　　| D 　　|

| E 　　| E 　　| D 　　| D 　　|

| C 　　| C 　　| Bm7 　| Bm7 　‖

| Em G5 | D 　A5 | Em G5 | D 　A5 ‖

Outro

　　　　　Em　　　　　G5　D　A5
　I'm gonna run to you,

　　　　　　　Em　　　　G5　D　A5
‖: I'm gonna run to you,

　　　　　　　　Em　　　G5　　　　　D　　　　A5
'Cause when the feeling's right, I'm gonna run all night,

　　　　　　　Em　　　　G5　D　A5
I'm gonna run to you. 　　　　　　:‖　*Repeat to fade*

4 Somebody

THE SECOND SINGLE from the classic 1985 album *Reckless* shows Bryan at his stadium-rocking best. Bryan's big, open G-A-C-D chords contrast with Keith Scott's subtle palm-mutes and bends in the main riff to make 'Somebody' a high point of every Adams gig.

▼A minor pentatonic scale

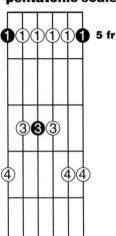

How to play it
The main riff (see TAB) uses the A minor pentatonic scale at the 5th fret. The letters 'PM' on the first two notes stand for Palm Mute – rest the edge of your picking hand on the strings near the bridge while you pick the first two notes so they're cut short. The sparse sound of the guitar chords in the verses is due to Bryan's Fsus2 chord. If you slide this chord shape two frets higher and keep the open third string, you get the G5 chord in bar 2. Remember that the rhythm guitar part should miss out the bass (6th) string throughout the verse.

Guitar solo
The first guitar solo is simply a repeat of the intro riff; the second features improvised ideas around the same chords. To make up your own solo in this section, use the A minor pentatonic scale (see fretbox). For added effect, try bending up the 8th fret on the second string and the 7th fret on the third string.

Guitar sound
There are two main guitar sounds used in the track. The rhythm guitars use a slightly distorted bridge-pickup sound with much of the bass end turned down and a short reverb added. The lead guitar also uses the bridge pickup, but with heavier levels of distortion and a thicker reverb. Avoid using high levels of delay on the rhythm sounds or you'll clutter up the chords in the mix.

▼ Intro and main riff

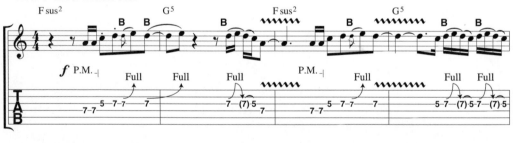

"Suddenly, we were selling out arenas when we were used to playing small theatres and clubs. We weren't doing anything different; it was just our time and people liked it."

4 Somebody

Words & Music by Bryan Adams & Jim Vallance

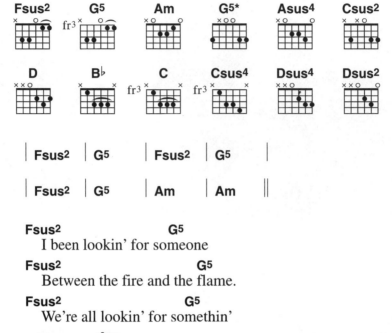

Fsus2	G5	Am	G5*	Asus4	Csus2
D	B♭	C	Csus4	Dsus4	Dsus2

Intro | **Fsus2** | **G5** | **Fsus2** | **G5** |

| **Fsus2** | **G5** | **Am** | **Am** ||

Verse 1

Fsus2   **G5**
  I been lookin' for someone

Fsus2   **G5**
  Between the fire and the flame.

Fsus2   **G5**
  We're all lookin' for somethin'

            Am
To ease the pain.

Verse 2

Fsus2   **G5**
  Now, who can you turn to

Fsus2   **G5**
  When it's all black and white

Fsus2   **G5**
  And the winners are losers

            Am
You see it every night.

Chorus 1

G5* Asus4   **Csus2**
  I need somebody,

D   **G5***
  Somebody like you,

          Asus4   **Csus2** **D**
Everybody needs somebody.

cont.

G5*   Asus4   Csus2
  I need somebody.

D   G5*
  Hey, what about you?

             Asus4   Csus2 D
Everybody needs somebody.

Riff | Fsus2 | G5 | Fsus2 | G5 | Fsus2 | G5 | Am | Am ||

Verse 3

Fsus2   G5
  When you're out on the front line

Fsus2   G5
  And you're watchin' them fall,

Fsus2   G5
  It doesn't take long to realise

             Am
It ain't worth fightin' for.

Verse 4

Fsus2   G5
  I thought I saw the Madonna

Fsus2   G5
  When you walked in the room,

Fsus2   G5
  Well, your eyes were like diamonds

             Am
And they cut right through, oh they cut right through.

Chorus 2   As Chorus 1

Solo | Fsus2 | G5 | Fsus2 | G5 | Fsus2 | G5 |

             | Fsus2 | G5 | Fsus2 | G5 | Am | Am ||

Bridge

B♭   C
  Another night, another lesson learned,

B♭   C Csus4 C
  It's the distance keeps us sane,

B♭   C
  But when the silence leads to sorrow

          Dsus4 D   Dsus2   D
We do it all again, all again.

Chorus 2   ‖: As Chorus 1 :‖ *Repeat to fade*

(5) Summer Of '69

IF A GUITARIST was asked to name one Bryan Adams track, it would be 'Summer Of '69'. Apart from the fact that the very first line mentions a guitar, the song has an instantly identifiable riff, a driving rock rhythm guitar part, and (most importantly) an endless solo over the outro. Bryan modestly describes it as "right for its time" but there are many working pub rock bands today who would disagree.

▼D fingering for chorus riff

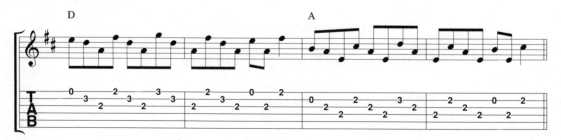

How to play it
If you haven't mastered palm mutes yet (see page 7) now is the time to put in some extra practice. The intro and whole first verse rely on the picking hand resting lightly on the strings as you play all downstrokes with the plectrum. Make sure you only play the lower two or three strings of the chord at the start – this gives you room to play more aggressively in the later stages of the song. The pre-chorus "when I look back now" section uses arpeggiated chords – i.e. single notes of the chord, picked one at a time with the plectrum. Don't be tempted to strum this section at all, even if you find it easier than picking individual notes.

The chorus riff
The chorus riff (see TAB) comes in after "best days of my life" and is actually easier to play than it first appears. All of the notes are based on a chord of D, with only the notes on the first (thinnest) string changing while the rest of the chord is held down. With practice, you can play the whole riff by picking across a chord of D, adding and removing the second and fourth finger to create the different top notes.

Guitar sound
Bryan's "first real six string" (or at least one of them) was a 1960 cherry red sunburst Strat, and you should be aiming for a single-coil pickup guitar sound, or at least an amp tone with the bass rolled off. Add distortion, preferably from the amplifier rather than an effects pedal, and a little reverb, but beyond that, avoid any other effects (particularly chorus). The 'big' guitar sound on the original and on our special CD soundalike was actually created by multi-tracking – i.e. recording the same guitar part twice.

▼ Main chorus riff

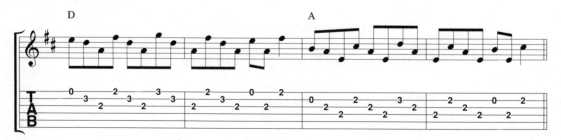

"One thing people never got though, was the song isn't about the actual *year* '69..."

5 Summer Of '69

Words & Music by Bryan Adams & Jim Vallance

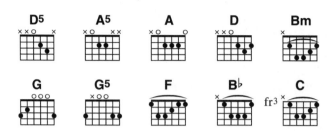

Intro | **D5** | **D5** ||

Verse 1
  D5   **A5**
I got my first real six-string, bought it at the five-and-dime.
  D5   **A**
Played it 'til my fingers bled, it was the summer of sixty-nine.

Verse 2
    D   **A**
Me and some guys from school had a band and we tried real hard.
    D
Jimmy quit and Jody got married,
    A
I should've known we'd never get far.

Chorus 1
  Bm   **A**
Oh, when I look back now,
  D   **G**
That summer seemed to last forever,
  Bm   **A**
And if I had the choice
  D   **G**
Yeah, I'd always wanna be there.
  Bm   **A**   **D(riff)**   **A**
Those were the best days of my life.

Verse 3
    D   **A**
Ain't no use in complainin' when you got a job to do.
    D
Spent my evenings down at the drive-in,
    A
And that's when I met you, yeah!

Chorus 2

Bm   A
Standin' on your Mama's porch,
D   G
You told me that you'd wait forever.
Bm   A
Oh, and when you held my hand
D   G
I knew that it was now or never.
Bm   A   D(riff) A
Those were the best days of my life, oh yeah
          D(riff)   A
Back in the summer of sixty-nine.

Bridge

F   B♭   C
Man, we were killin' time, we were young and restless,
  B♭
We needed to unwind.
F   B♭   C
I guess nothin' can last forever, forever, no.

| D(riff) | D(riff) | A | A | D(riff) | D(riff) | A | A   ‖

Verse 4

D
And now the times are changin',
A
Look at everything that's come and gone.
D
Sometimes when I play that old six-string
A
I think about you, wonder what went wrong.

Chorus 3

Bm   A
Standin' on your Mama's porch,
D   G
You told me it would last forever.
Bm   A
Oh, and when you held my hand,
D   G
I knew that it was now or never.
Bm   A   D(riff) A
Those were the best days of my life, oh yeah
          D(riff)   A
Back in the summer of sixty-nine.

Coda

| D | D | A | A ‖
Play riff with vocal to fade ad lib.

6 (Everything I Do) I Do For You

ANY GUITARIST who was around in 1991 (or indeed, anyone else) could not fail to have noticed this international number 1. It was written for the film *Robin Hood (Prince of Thieves)* and is Bryan's most successful song.

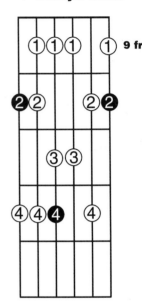

▼ **D major scale**

How to play it
The first thing you'll notice about the chords is the symbol /D after the first few chord names in the verse. This is a 'pedal note' (actually played by the piano on the recording). If you want to simulate the left hand of the piano on an unaccompanied guitar, just play the chords with the open fourth string ringing out – see the chord boxes over the page. Note that the spacious 'synth' sound of the intro and first verse is actually a guitar with a volume swell at the start of each chord. If you haven't got access to a volume pedal or 'slow attack' effect, try leaving the piano unaccompanied for the first verse, then come in with the single strum of D at the start of verse 2.

Guitar solo
Keith's solo is based on the D major scale, which is one of the reasons it sounds so melodic. Shown on the right is a fretbox for this scale. If you want to try improvising using these notes, bear in mind that one of the strengths of the original solo is its use of phrasing – i.e. leaving gaps in between solo lines, and letting some notes ring out for 2 or 3 whole beats.

Guitar sound
There are four guitar parts on the recording – an acoustic 12-string playing chords, two distorted electrics for the power chords and solo parts, and the slow attack/volume pedal effect from the intro. To play along with the recording, use a slightly distorted sound, through an amp if possible (Bryan and Keith used HiWatt, Marshall and Vox valve amps on the original recording). Add reverb throughout, then kick in a medium-length delay (around 300ms) for the middle 8 section.

"It's actually a beautiful song to sing live."

6 (Everything I Do) I Do It For You

Words by Bryan Adams & Robert John Lange
Music by Michael Kamen

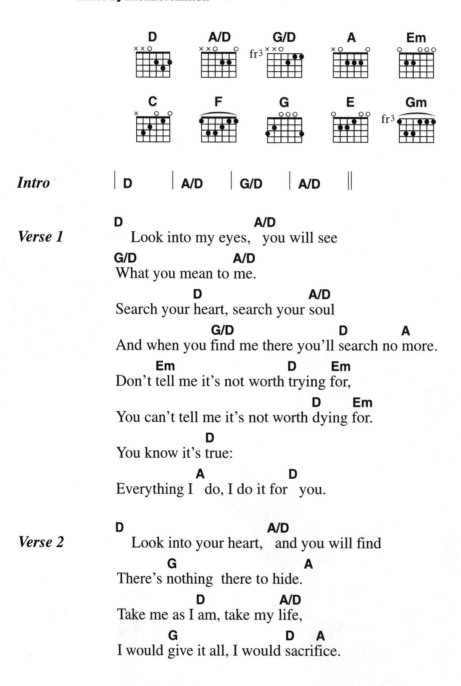

Intro | D | A/D | G/D | A/D ||

Verse 1

    D   A/D
    Look into my eyes,   you will see
G/D   A/D
What you mean to me.
                  D   A/D
Search your heart, search your soul
                    G/D   D   A
And when you find me there you'll search no more.
           Em   D   Em
Don't tell me it's not worth trying for,
                              D   Em
You can't tell me it's not worth dying for.
                D
You know it's true:
            A   D
Everything I do, I do it for you.

Verse 2

    D   A/D
    Look into your heart,   and you will find
           G   A
There's nothing there to hide.
                D   A/D
Take me as I am, take my life,
           G   D   A
I would give it all, I would sacrifice.

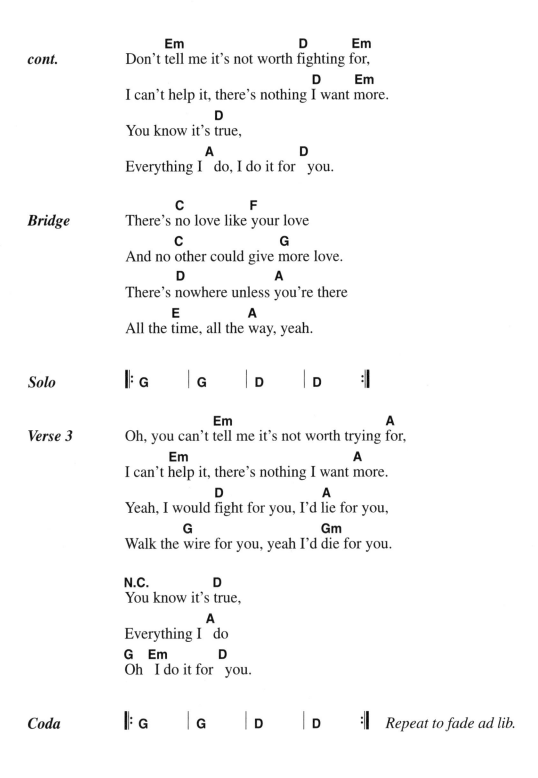

cont.

    Em   **D**   **Em**
Don't tell me it's not worth fighting for,

                       D   **Em**
I can't help it, there's nothing I want more.

         D
You know it's true,

      A   **D**
Everything I do, I do it for you.

Bridge

     C   **F**
There's no love like your love

     C   **G**
And no other could give more love.

     D   **A**
There's nowhere unless you're there

    E   **A**
All the time, all the way, yeah.

Solo

‖: **G** | **G** | **D** | **D**   :‖

Verse 3

            Em   **A**
Oh, you can't tell me it's not worth trying for,

    Em   **A**
I can't help it, there's nothing I want more.

     D   **A**
Yeah, I would fight for you, I'd lie for you,

    G   **Gm**
Walk the wire for you, yeah I'd die for you.

N.C.   **D**
You know it's true,

    A
Everything I do

G **Em**   **D**
Oh I do it for you.

Coda

‖: **G** | **G** | **D** | **D**   :‖ *Repeat to fade ad lib.*

7 Can't Stop This Thing We Started

THE SECOND SINGLE from the multi-platinum 1991 album *Waking Up The Neighbours* had Bryan back in chart-friendly pop mode. It follows the winning formula of many songs he's written with Mutt Lange – low-key verse leads into pre-chorus 'lift', peaking in a huge singalong chorus.

How to play it
The song's most distinctive feature is that opening riff, using a technique called cross-picking (literally, pick across the notes of the chord one by one). We've included the first six bars of the intro in the TAB below. It's tricky to play the exact rhythm of those notes at the high neck positions that Keith Scott uses, so if you have difficulty, try strumming a single chord per bar and let the CD part take over the cross-picked riffs.

The rhythm guitar part
On the verses, Bryan's rhythm part focuses mainly on the bass strings of the chords to leave space for the vocal. The pre-chorus section uses the same cross-picking as the intro (see TAB), building up into the powerful full-strummed chords of the chorus.

Guitar sound
Bryan recalls exactly which guitars were in the studio on the 'Can't Stop…' sessions. "I used a 1960 sunburst Gibson Les Paul into an AC-30 for all the rhythm tracks. Keith used a '59 SG Junior for the rhythm double, into the Marshall AC-30 combination of amps." And the solo? "Keith on my '62 Strat." For those of us without access to this kind of vintage gear, any reasonably powerful guitar should cover the basic rhythm sound. You'll get a fatter tone if you use a humbucking pickup (bridge position) into a slightly distorted amp setting. For the solo, switch to the neck pickup and increase the gain slightly, adding subtle delay at around 250ms.

▼ **Intro riff**

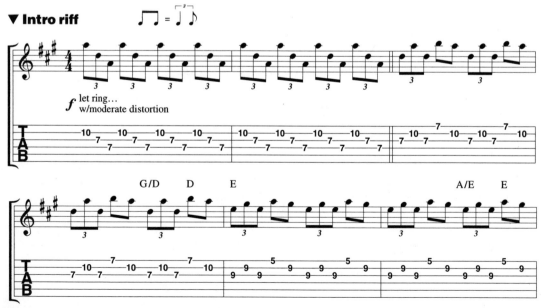

Can't Stop This Thing We Started

Words & Music by Bryan Adams & Robert John Lange

Chord diagrams: D5, D, E, A, D/A, Dsus2, F#m, B♭, F

Intro | D5 | D5 | D | D | E |

Yeah!

E   D   E
Baby   I'm coming to get you.

Verse 1

A   D/A
You might stop a hurricane,

A   D/A
Might even stop the driving rain.

A   D/A
You might have a dozen other guys

        A   D/A
But if you wanna stop me baby, don't even try.

        A   D   E
I'm going one way, your way.

                    D
Now it's such a strong way,

                    E
Let's make it our way, now baby!

Chorus 1

Dsus2   E   F#m
I can't stop this thing we started,

        Dsus2   A
You gotta know it's right.

Dsus2   E   F#m   Dsus2   A
I can't stop this course we've plotted,   yeah.

Can't Stop This Thing We Started

cont.

```
D                       E
  This thing called love, we got it,
F♯m                A
  No place for the broken-hearted.
Dsus2              E
  I can't stop this thing we started,
D                  E
No way, I'm going your way!
```

Verse 2

```
A                                        D/A
  You might stop the world spinning round,
A                             D/A
  Might even walk on holy ground.
A                           D/A
  I ain't Superman and I can't fly
     A                              D/A
But if you wanna stop me baby, don't even try.
     A        D    E
I'm going one way,   your way,
             D
It's such a strong way,
             E
Let's make it our way, now baby!
```

Chorus 2

```
Dsus2              E              F♯m
  I can't stop this thing we started,
          Dsus2   A
You gotta know it's right.
Dsus2              E                F♯m    Dsus2   A
  I can't stop this course we've plotted,   yeah.
D                  E
  This thing called love, we got it,
F♯m                A
  No place for the broken-hearted.
Dsus2              E
  I can't stop this thing we started,
D                  E
No way, I'm going your way!
```

30

Middle

Bb   F   Bb
Oh, why take it slow? I gotta know.

            A
Hey! 'Cause nothing can stop this thing that we got.

Solo

‖: D | E | F#m | A   :‖

Chorus 3

Dsus2   E   F#m
   I can't stop this thing we started,

            Dsus2   A
You gotta know it's right.

Dsus2   E   F#m   Dsus2   A
   I can't stop this course we've plotted,   oh - oh yeah.

Bb   C
   This thing called love, we got it,

F   Bb
   Ain't no place for the broken-hearted,

D   E
   I can't stop it,   I can't stop it.

Chorus 4

Dsus2   E   F#m
   I can't stop this thing we started,

            Dsus2   A
   You gotta know it's so right.

Dsus2   E   F#m   Dsus2 A
   I can't stop this course we've plotted,

Dsus2   E
   I can't stop it,   I can't stop it,

F#m   Dsus2   A
   I can't stop it.

Dsus2   E
   I can't stop it,   yeah.   *Fade out*

8 Have You Ever Really Loved a Woman?

THIS SPANISH-INFLUENCED ballad was written for the 1995 film *Don Juan DeMarco*, starring Johnny Depp. The song included flamenco virtuoso Paco De Lucia on the main guitar part. Bryan chose to take a back seat to Paco's guitar playing on the track, contenting himself with a simple strumming part in the choruses.

How to play it

Paco de Lucia's flamenco part is all played with fingers, and mainly concentrates on variations of the main melody. Unless you're a very experienced classical/fingerstyle player, the easiest way to play the song is to concentrate on a more rhythmic approach, aiming to cover Bryan's chord parts. Before attempting the whole song, practise strumming 6 to the bar using alternate up and downstrokes (i.e. DUDUDU for every bar). Ensure that the up and downstrokes are exactly even in terms of volume and timing.

Rhythm part variation

To add variation, you may want to arpeggiate the chords in the verses (see TAB). To do this, hold down the chord (e.g. E♭ at the start of the verse) and then pick across the fifth, fourth, third and second strings, letting the chord ring on for the rest of the bar. Repeat this with the Cm, D and B♭ chords as the verse develops. Just before the chorus, start to play the down-up strumming pattern you practised.

Guitar sound

There are four main guitar parts on the original recording (and on our CD re-recording). Paco's lead part is the loudest, with a second Spanish guitar playing chords underneath. Bryan plays the DUDUDU strumming pattern on a steel-string Epiphone acoustic with a plectrum.

In the middle 8 there's the obligatory power chord electric guitar, but very low in the mix. If you choose to play the classical/Spanish guitar parts, use fingernails and thumb only for maximum authenticity.

▼ Verse accompaniment

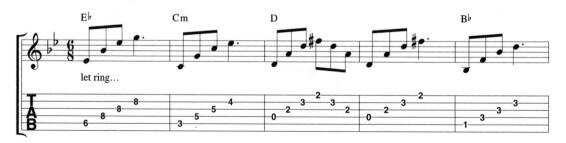

Have You Ever Really Loved a Woman?

Words & Music by Bryan Adams, Robert John Lange & Michael Kamen

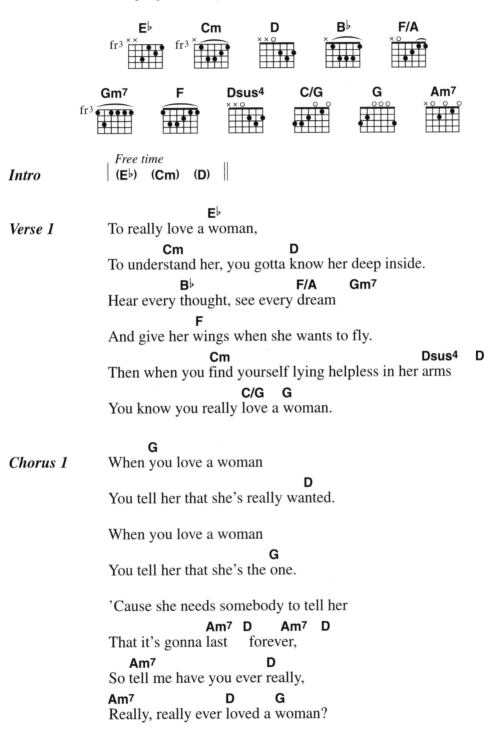

Intro

Free time

| (E♭) (Cm)   (D) ‖

Verse 1

                   E♭
To really love a woman,

        Cm   D
To understand her, you gotta know her deep inside.

          B♭   F/A   Gm7
Hear every thought, see every dream

          F
And give her wings when she wants to fly.

           Cm   Dsus4   D
Then when you find yourself lying helpless in her arms

           C/G   G
You know you really love a woman.

Chorus 1

      G
When you love a woman

                       D
You tell her that she's really wanted.

When you love a woman

                G
You tell her that she's the one.

'Cause she needs somebody to tell her

           Am7 D   Am7   D
That it's gonna last   forever,

    Am7   D
So tell me have you ever really,

Am7   D   G
Really, really ever loved a woman?

33

Have You Ever Really Loved a Woman?

Verse 2

E♭
To really love a woman

Cm   D
Let her hold you till you know how she needs to be touched.

B♭   F/A   Gm7
You've gotta breathe her, really taste her

F
Till you can feel her in your blood.

Cm   Dsus4 D
And when you can see your unborn children in her eyes

C/G   G
You know you really love a woman.

Chorus 2

G
When you love a woman

D
You tell her that she's really wanted.

When you love a woman

G
You tell her that she's the one.

'Cause she needs somebody to tell her

Am7 D   Am7   D
That you'll always be   together.

Am7   D
So tell me have you ever really,

Am7   D   G
Really, really ever loved a woman?

Bridge

E♭   F
You got to give her some faith, hold her tight,

G
A little tenderness, gotta treat her right.

D   G
She will be there for you, taking good care of you,

You really gotta love your woman.

Solo | E♭ | Cm | D |

           | D   B♭ F | B♭ | F/A Gm⁷ | F ||

Link

     F   Cm   Dsus⁴ D

And when you find yourself lyin' helpless in her arms

                    C/G   G

You know you really love   a woman.

Chorus 3

             G

When you love a woman

                           D

You tell her that she's really wanted.

When you love a woman

                     G

You tell her that she's the one.

'Cause she needs somebody to tell her

                Am⁷ D   Am⁷ D

That it's gonna last   forever,

     Am⁷   D

So tell me have you ever really,

 Am⁷   D   G

Really, really ever loved a woman?

Coda

           Am⁷   D

Just tell me have you ever really,

 Am⁷   D   G

Really, really ever loved a woman?

           Am⁷   D

Just tell me have you ever really,

 Am⁷   D   G

Really, really ever loved a woman?

9 (I Wanna Be) Your Underwear

EVERY NOW AND THEN Bryan writes a slightly tongue-in-cheek number, reminding us that he doesn't take himself too seriously. '(I Wanna Be) Your Underwear' features high vocals and distorted rhythm guitar riffs that wouldn't be out of place in an AC/DC song.

How to play it
This type of rock rhythm guitar playing only works if you use power chords (labelled as '5' chords in the chord sheet). In most rock tracks, this means playing only two or three strings from the bass end of each chord. It's also worth noting that although the rhythm guitar is fairly *loud* it's not particularly *busy* i.e. it usually only plays one or two strums per bar. The tempo and groove of the song is carried along by the vocal and drums. Listen to the CD carefully to hear when the guitar plays the rhythmic 'stabs' that characterise the backing, and try to copy these exactly. To get you started, we've supplied TAB for the stabs that are used at the start of each chorus.

▼ **G major**

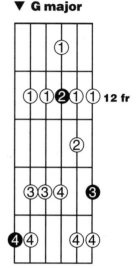

Guitar solo
Keith Scott's solo begins with some mad pitch bend effects, before going into a more melodic section taking some of its notes from the G major scale (see fretbox). The solo overlaps into the 'sleeping bag' middle 8 section before dropping back into the final chorus.

Guitar sound
Bryan: "I used my Strat again into an AC-30 and Keith used a few different guitars for different parts: a '62 Strat, a Gretsch 6120 and a black Paul Reed Smith guitar. They went into a combination of an AC-30, a Marshall 100 watt Plexi head and a Fender Tweed Bassman." The rhythm guitar parts should be a bright bridge pickup sound with the tone controls up full, medium distortion and short reverb added. The lead parts use a similar sound but also feature a wah-wah pedal.

▼ **Chorus**

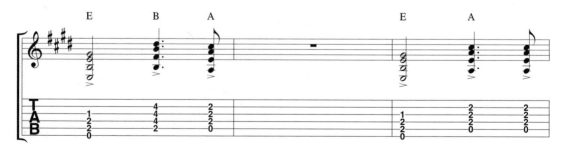

"What's important to me is having a good time with my music, which is what I love to do."

9 (I Wanna Be) Your Underwear

Words & Music by Bryan Adams & Robert John Lange

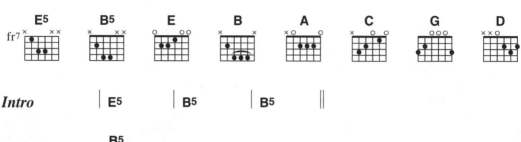

| E5 | B5 | E | B | A | C | G | D |

Intro | E5 | B5 | B5   ‖

Verse 1

B5
I wanna be your t-shirt when it's wet;

Wanna be the shower when you sweat;

I gotta to be the tattoo on your skin;

Yeah let me be your bed, baby, when you climb in.

I wanna be the sheets when you sleep;

Let me be the secrets that you keep;

I gotta to be the spoon to stir your cream;

I wanna be the one that really makes you scream.

Chorus 1

E B   A   E A
I wanna be your lipstick   when you lick it;
E B   A   E A
I wanna be your high heels   when you kick it;
E B   A   E A
I wanna be your sweet love, babe,   yeah when you make it;
A
From your feet up to your hair,
B5
More than anything I swear
A   E5
I wanna be your underwear.

Verse 2

B5
I wanna be the itch that you scratch;

Wanna be the chair when you relax;

I got to be your razor when you shave;

Wanna be the habit that really makes you crave.

Chorus 2

E B   A   E A
I   wanna be your hot-tub   when you're dippin';
E B   A   E A
I   wanna be your bathrobe   when you're drippin';
E B   A   E A
I   wanna be your cocktail, baby,   when you're sippin';
A
I just wanna be right there,
B
More than anything I swear
A   **E5**   **B5**
I wanna be your underwear.

Solo

| C | G | D | G | |
| C | G | D | G | ||

Bridge

    C   **G**   **D**   **G**
I wanna be your sleepin' bag, baby slip inside;
    C   **G**   **B5**   **E5**
Let me be your motorcycle 'n' take you for a ride, alright.

Chorus 3

E B   A   E A
I   wanna be your hot sauce   yeah, when you're cookin';
E B   A   E A
I   wanna be your sunglasses,   hey, good lookin';
E B   A   E A
I   wanna be, wanna be the one,   yeah, you stick your hook in.
A
I just wanna be right there;
B5
More than anything I swear;
A   **N.C.**
Oh yeah,   I wanna be your underwear.

10 The Only Thing That Looks Good on Me is You

BRYAN'S CO-WRITER, Mutt Lange, has also been responsible for writing and producing material for many other famous names including Def Leppard, Shania Twain and AC/DC, and his influence can be heard throughout this track. It's also a rare example of Bryan contributing the lead guitar licks, leaving Keith to play more straightforward backing parts in the intro and verses.

How to play it

The song is almost entirely based on a 2-bar loop of the chords D, C and G. Rather than simply strumming these (feel free to give this a try – but it sounds 'a little bit Country'!) you should play the computer sequencer-style verse riff throughout this section (shown below). On the original, Mutt Lange plays the riff himself, using his thumb and first finger to pick two notes at a time. If you find the fingerstyle riff too difficult, try using downstrokes with the plectrum (again, hitting only the two lowest-sounding notes of the chord) while you play the chords D, C and G.

    The lead riff (see TAB) is played by Bryan on the intro and outro, and features a slide or 'gliss' up to the first note. It includes a double-stop (i.e. hitting two strings at once) for the last note.

Guitar sound

As usual, Bryan demonstrates his elephantine recollection of the gear used in the recording; "I'm playing the intro lead licks on my 1960 Fender Strat into a Mutron 3 [envelope shaper pedal] and then going into my AC-30. The 'jangle' in the middle 8 was Keith on a Fender villager 12 string." The Mutron 3 is actually only used to provide subtle tone shaping for the main riff, so a wah-wah pedal in a fixed setting or even a soft tone control setting should do the job here. Use the bridge pickup for all the guitar parts, and a fairly high-gain distortion setting to compensate for the delicate picking you're using on the verse riff.

▼ Verse riff

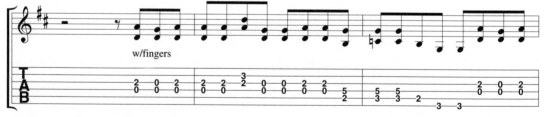

▼ Intro and outro riff

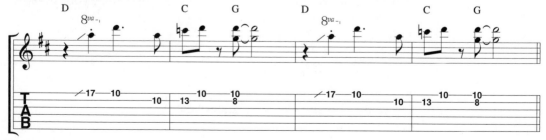

"I'm playing the intro lead licks on my 1960 Fender Strat into a Mutron 3 and then going into my AC-30."

10 The Only Thing That Looks Good on Me is You

Words & Music by Bryan Adams & Robert John Lange

D7   C   G   D   F   B♭   A   Dm7

Intro   2 bars drums | D7 | C G | D7 | C G | D7 | C G ‖

Verse 1
          D   C   G
Well I don't look good in no Armani Suits,
      D   C   G
No Gucci shoes or designer boots.
       D   C   G
I've tried the latest lines from A to Z
           D   C   G
But there's just one thing that looks good on me.

Chorus 1
D7   C   G
  The only thing I want,
D7   C   G
  The only thing I need,
D7   C   G
  The only thing I choose,
      F   N.C.
The only thing that looks good on me is (you.)

 | D7 | C G | D7 | C G ‖
  you.

Verse 2
          D   C   G
I'm not satisfied with Versace style,
           D   C   G
Put those patent leather pants in the circular file.
      D   C   G
Sometimes I think I might be   looking good
           D   C   G
But there's only one thing that fits like it should.

Chorus 2

D⁷   C   G
   The only thing I want,

D⁷   C   G
   The only thing I need,

D⁷   C   G
   The only thing I choose,

          F   N.C.
The only thing that looks good on me is (you.)

| D⁷ | C G | D⁷ | C G ‖
you.

Middle

                F   C
Yeah it's you, it could only be you,

                      B♭
Nobody else will ever   do.

                    F   A
Yeah, baby it's you that I stick to.

| D⁷ | C   G | D⁷ | C G ‖
     Yeah, we stick like glue.

Chorus 3

D⁷   C   G
   The only thing I want,

D⁷   C   G
   The only thing I need,

D⁷   C   G
   The only thing I choose,

        Dm⁷   C   G   D⁷
The only thing that looks good on me is you.

Chorus 4

     D⁷   C   G
‖:   The only thing I want,

D⁷   C   G
   The only thing I need,

D⁷   C   G
   The only thing I choose,

        D⁷   C   G   D⁷
The only thing that looks good on me is you. :‖

Coda

‖: D⁷ | C G | D⁷ | C G :‖ *Repeat to fade*
                                          with vocal ad lib.

11 18 'Till I Die

THE TITLE TRACK of Bryan's 1996 number 1 album, according to him, sums up his attitude to music and life in general. Given that his other main interest outside of music is gardening, the phrase "18 till I die" might be difficult to justify, but if the man can write great rock tracks like this, we can surely forgive him the occasional lapse?

How to play it

The main riff (see TAB) is played with a plectrum, using cross-picking and two pull-offs. These are quite difficult to play at speed, so make sure you fret every note as cleanly as possible, ensuring that each of the open notes rings on clearly. Keep playing the riff for the first eight bars of the verse, then leave a space for the high vocal "18 till I die", giving you time to move up to the ninth fret ready for the E chord shape.

The chorus

The chorus changes into the key of D, and Bryan's rhythm part plays a simple down-and-up strumming pattern with an emphasis on the downstrokes. For the three-bar "don't worry 'bout the future" middle section, the strumming gets less busy, concentrating on one chord per bar, then leads back into the main riff for four bars, ending with the final chorus repeats.

Guitar sound

The Strat and Vox combination is still Bryan's most used setup; "I played the rhythm and lead on my 1960 Fender Cherry Sunburst into my fave AC-30. The little licks in the second verse were Keith on his Gretsch 6120" . Several of the guitars were double-tracked on the original. To simulate the sound of more than one guitar, try a chorus pedal or very short delay setting (less than 80ms).

▼ Main riff

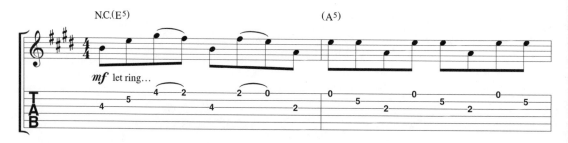

"It's not so much that I'm writing literally about age as I am an attitude. That attitude extends a lot further than rock 'n' roll."

11 18 'Till I Die

Words & Music by Bryan Adams & Robert John Lange

E	A	B	D	D/F#	G	Em7	G/D	F#m

Intro | E | A | E | A ||

Verse 1
         E   A
Wanna be young the rest of my life,

E   A
Never say no, try anything twice.

      E   A
Till the angels come and ask me to fly,

        E   A   N.C.
Gonna be eighteen till I die, eighteen till I die.

E   B   A   D
   Can't live forever,   that's wishful thinking,

E   B A   D
   Who ever said that   must've been drinking.

E   B A
   Don't wanna grow up,   I don't see why.

G   A
   I couldn't care less if time flies by.

Chorus 1
D   D/F# G   Em7   A
Eighteen till I die, gonna be eighteen till I die,

          D   G/D
Yeah, it sure feels good to be alive.

Em7   A
Someday I'll be eighteen going on fifty-five.

D   D/F# G   A
Eighteen till I die, alright.

Verse 2
   E   A
   Anyway, I just wanna say

E   A
   Why bother with what happened yesterday?

   E   A
It's not my style, I live for the minute.

      E   A   N.C.
If you wanna stay young, get both feet in it, eighteen till I die.

cont.

E   B A   D
 A little bit of this, a little bit of that,

E   B A   D
 A little bit of everything, gotta get on track.

 E   B   A
It's not how you look, it's what you feel inside,

 G   A
I don't care when, I don't need to know why.

Chorus 2

D D/F♯ G   Em⁷   A
Eighteen till I die, gonna be eighteen till I die,

    D   G/D
Yeah, it sure feels good to be alive.

Em⁷   A
Someday I'll be eighteen going on fifty-five.

D D/F♯ G   A
Eighteen till I die, there's one thing for sure, I'm sure gonna try.

Solo   ‖: D | G/D | Em⁷ | A :‖

Bridge

     Em⁷   F♯m
Yeah, don't worry about the future, forget about the past.

G
 Gonna have a ball, yeah,

E   A | E | E ‖
 We're gonna have a blast, gonna make it last.

Chorus 3

D D/F♯ G   Em⁷   A
Eighteen till I die, gonna be eighteen till I die,

    D   G/D
Yeah, it sure feels good to be alive.

Em⁷   A
Someday I'll be eighteen going on fifty-five.

D   D/F♯ G
Eighteen till I die,

     D   N.C. G/D | D D/F♯ | G ‖
Gonna be eighteen till I die, alright!

Coda

     D   D/F♯ G
I'm gonna be eighteen till I die, alright!

D G/D   D   G/D D D/F♯ G
 Oh yeah, oh yeah, oh, eighteen till I die.

12 When You're Gone

BRYAN'S MOST SUCCESSFUL single of 1998 featured ex-Spice Girl Melanie C as co-vocalist. "We were both in the same hotel and we met in the elevator. I'd just written 'When You're Gone' and I asked her if she wanted to sing it with me. People said: 'why are you recording something with a Spice Girl?' Everyone thought that I was mad!"

How to play it
The song is in the key of C, but many of the riffs sound better in A, so Keith Scott uses a capo at the 3rd fret on one of the rhythm guitar parts. Our chord sheet shows the chords as they actually sound – i.e. in the key of C.

Rhythm guitar part
The rhythm guitar part uses a particular pattern that avoids straightforward down-up strumming throughout. Note that the second beat of each bar is accented with a particularly strong down-strum. Also, each F chord in the chorus arrives slightly early (on a plectrum upstroke) – these are called 'pushes', where some instruments make a chord change just before the barline.

Guitar sound
Appropriately for late '90s rock, the guitar sounds are quite understated – usually just an amp on a 'crunch' distortion setting with no other effects added apart from reverb. Both Bryan and Keith were playing vintage instruments; "I used my '62 Strat into a fawn AC-30. Keith was on a '54 blond Telecaster into a tweed Bandmaster... he kicked in a Tube Screamer [Ibanez distortion pedal] for the solo which was kept from the basic track."

▼ Intro riff

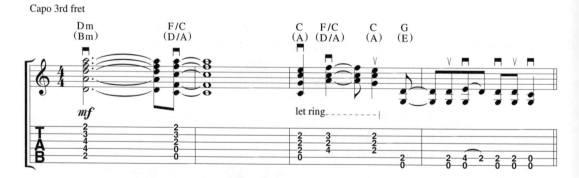

"People said: 'why are you recording something with a Spice Girl?' Everyone thought that I was mad!"

12 When You're Gone

Words & Music by Bryan Adams & Eliot Kennedy

Intro | Dm | F | C | G ||

Verse 1
          Dm   **G**
I've been wandering around the house all night
  C
Wondering what the hell to do.
     Dm   **G**   **C**
Yeah, I'm trying to concentrate but all I can think of is you.
     Dm   **G**
Well the phone don't ring 'cause my friends ain't home,
  C
I'm tired of being all alone.
     Dm   **B♭**   **G**
Got the T.V. on 'cause the radio's playing songs

That remind me of you.

Chorus 1
      Dm
Baby when you're gone
F   **C** **G**
 I realize I'm in love.
      Dm
The days go on and on
F   **C** **G**
 And the nights just seem so long.
        Dm
Even food don't taste that good,
F   **C** **G**
 Drink ain't doing what it should.
      Dm
Things just feel so wrong,
B♭   **G**
 Baby when you're gone.

Verse 2

         Dm   **G**
I've been driving up and down these streets

   C
Trying to find somewhere to go.

        Dm   **G**   **C**
Yeah, I'm looking for a familiar face but there's no one I know.

      Dm   **G**
Ah, this is torture, this is pain,

   C
It feels like I'm gonna go insane.

     Dm   **B♭**
I hope you're coming back real soon,

     G
'Cause I don't know what to do.

Chorus 2   As Chorus 1

Solo   ‖: **Dm** | **G** | **C** | **C** :‖ *Play 3 times*

        | **Dm** | **B♭** | **G** | **G** | ‖

Chorus 3

               Dm
Baby when you're gone

F   **C**   **G**
  I realize I'm in love.

             Dm
The days go on and on

F   **C**   **G**
  And the nights just seem so   long.

              Dm
Even food don't taste that good,

F   **C**   **G**
  Drink ain't doing what it should.

            Dm
Things just feel so wrong,

B♭   **G**
  Baby when you're gone.

          Dm
Baby when you're gone,

B♭   **F**
  Yeah, baby when you're gone.

13 Cloud Number Nine

THIS, THE THIRD SINGLE from the album *On a Day Like Today*, is described by Bryan as "straight ahead pop-rock". It's a rare example of one of his songs getting a substantial remix treatment using a sampler, even to the point of different chords in the single version. Our version is faithful to the recording on the album. For all the live shows during this period, Bryan was actually playing bass, leaving guitar duties entirely to Keith.

▼ D major scale

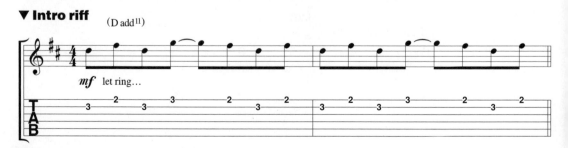

How to play it
The intro riff (see TAB) is simply a chord of D, with the little finger added at the third fret of the first string half-way through the bar then taken off again. Pick the first two strings with a plectrum fairly delicately to get the timing accurate.

    The main rhythm part in the song is played on an acoustic, using even down-and-up strokes throughout. Be careful, though – the song is in the key of D, making it all too easy to strike the unwanted sixth and fifth strings when you're strumming from the elbow. Bryan's acoustic guitar technique often involves muting these notes with his thumb over the top of the neck. If you can't manage this, make sure you strum those four-string D chords as accurately as you can.

Guitar solo
Keith Scott's guitar solo uses a bottleneck slide, and most of the time he's sliding into – or out of – notes of the currently chord shape. The bottleneck solo can be played without any special tunings, but make sure you have perfected the technique of muting unwanted strings or you'll end up with wrong notes ringing out. If you want to try a solo without slide, we've shown the D major scale (see fretbox) – use notes from this scale to improvise around the chords shown.

Guitar sound
Keith was using a 1964 Strat into a Tweed Fender Bassman, Marshall head and Vox combo. Bryan's contributions came from a Gibson acoustic and a Fender Precision bass. Despite the up-tempo feel, don't be tempted to spoil the detail of the main riff with too much distortion. If you must stomp on a pedal, save it for the guitar solo, when the extra gain will help to add sustain.

▼ Intro riff   (D add¹¹)

mf   let ring…

13 Cloud Number Nine

Words & Music by Bryan Adams, Max Martin & Gretchen Peters

| D | G | Asus⁴ | Em | A | Bm | B♭ |

Intro | D | D ||

Verse 1
     D
Clue number one was when you knocked on my door,
Em
Clue number two was the look that you wore,
    Asus⁴   **A**
And that's when I knew it was a pretty good sign
     G   **D**
That something was wrong up on cloud number nine.

Pre-chorus 1
          A
Well it's a long way up

                 D
And we won't come down tonight,
     A
Well it may be wrong
               G   **A**
But baby it sure feels right.

Chorus 1
          D
And the moon is out and the stars are bright
          Em
And whatever comes gonna be alright,
        A   **G**   **D**
'Cause tonight you will be mine   up on cloud number nine.

And there ain't no place that I'd rather be,
        Em
And we can't go back but you're here with me.
      A   **G**   **D**
Yeah, the weather is really fine   up on cloud number nine.

Verse 2

A   D
Now he hurt you and you hurt me

Em
And that wasn't the way it was supposed to be,

Asus⁴   A
So baby tonight let's leave the   world behind

G   D
And spend some time up on cloud number nine.

Pre-chorus 2   As Pre-chorus 1

Chorus 2   As Chorus 1

Link | D | D | Bm | Bm | B♭ | B♭ |

Bridge

              A
Well we won't come down tonight,

Yeah, we won't come down tonight,

No, we won't come down tonight.

Chorus 3

              D
'Cause the moon is out and the stars are bright

Em
And whatever comes gonna be alright,

        A   G   D
'Cause tonight you will be mine   up on cloud number nine.

And there ain't no place that I'd rather be,

          Em
And we can't go back but you're here with me.

        A   G   D
Yeah, the weather is really fine   up on cloud number nine.

        A   G
Yeah, we can watch the world go by

        D   G   A   D
Up on cloud number nine.

Further Reading

If you've enjoyed this book why not check out some of the great titles below. They are available from all good music retailers and book shops, or you can visit our website: www.musicsales.com. In case of difficulty please contact Music Sales direct (see page 2).

The Chord Songbook Series

Play all your favourite hits with just a few easy chords for each song! Huge range of titles to choose from, including:

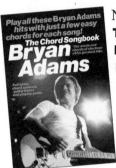

NEW! **Abba** AM959740
The Beatles NO90664
Blur AM936914
Bon Jovi AM936892
Boyzone AM956956
Bryan Adams
AM963490
Eric Clapton
AM956054
The Corrs AM956967
The Cranberries
AM944383
The Levellers
AM951445
Metallica AM944680
Alanis Morissette
AM944086
Oasis AM936903
Oasis 2 AM951478
Pulp AM942678
Stereophonics
AM956065
Sting AM940489
Stone Roses AM951500
Paul Weller AM942546
Wet Wet Wet
AM938135
The Who AM956021

Play Guitar With...Series

Play guitar and sing along with the specially-recorded CD backing tracks for classic songs from your favourite bands. Here are just some of the titles in this superb series.

The Beatles NO90665
The Beatles Book 2
NO90667
The Beatles Book 3
NO90689
Blur AM935320
Bon Jovi AM92558
Bryan Adams – The Early Years
AM970475
Bryan Adams
AM963380
Eric Clapton
AM950862
Eric Clapton Book 2
AM962896
The Kinks AM951863
Kula Shaker
AM943767
Metallica AM92559
Oasis AM935330
Ocean Colour Scene
AM943712
Stereophonics
AM960950
Sting AM968000
The Stone Roses
AM943701

...plus many more
titles for you to collect!